The Promise of the Rainbow

BY MIIKO SHAFFIER
co-written by Chana Grosser

Illustrated by: Dmitry Gitelman (diemgi.com)
Layout & Design by: Ken Parker (visual-variables.com)

Published by:
Shefer Publishing
www.SheferPublishing.com

For permissions, comments and ordering information write:
Miiko@LearnHebrew.tv

ISBN 978-1-958999-06-6

THE PROMISE
OF THE RAINBOW

an **EASY EEVREET STORY**

BY MIIKO SHAFFIER

SHEFER

PUBLISHING

Based on Genesis Chapter 6-9
This story can be read like any English story book.
When you get to a Hebrew word, do your best to
sound it out and guess the meaning. You can check the
pronunciation and meaning in the back of the book.

HAVE FUN!

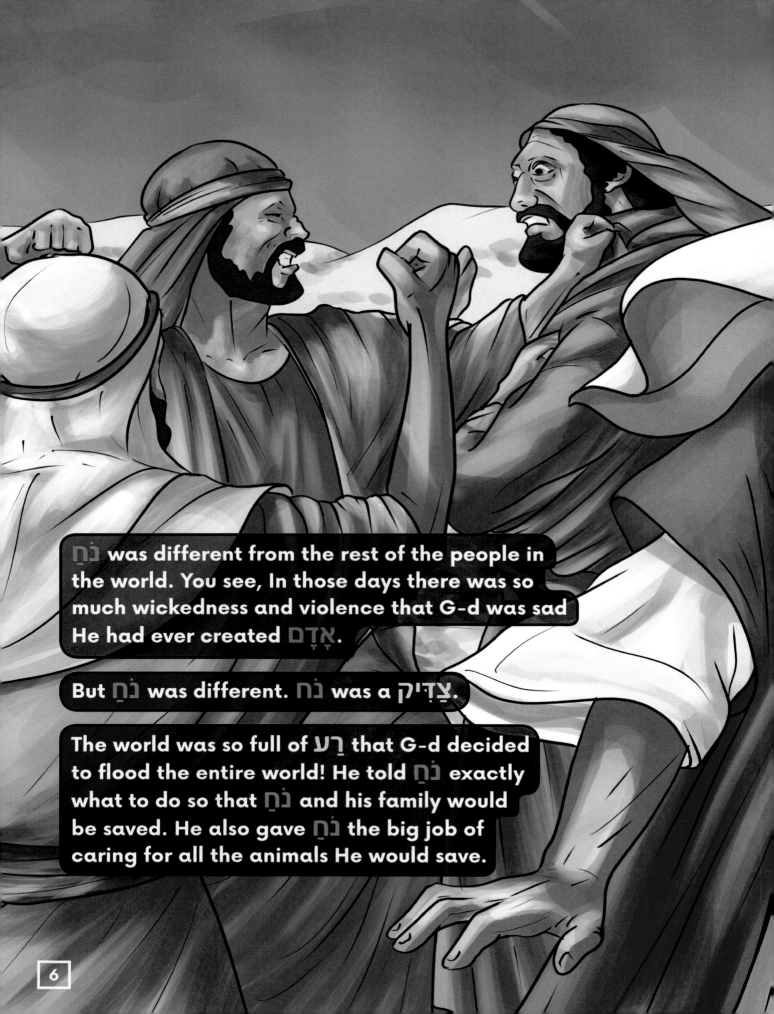

נֹחַ was different from the rest of the people in the world. You see, In those days there was so much wickedness and violence that G-d was sad He had ever created אָדָם.

But נֹחַ was different. נֹחַ was a צַדִּיק.

The world was so full of רַע that G-d decided to flood the entire world! He told נֹחַ exactly what to do so that נֹחַ and his family would be saved. He also gave נֹחַ the big job of caring for all the animals He would save.

G-d told נֹחַ
"Make a huge תֵּבָה with many rooms.
Cover the walls inside and out with tar.
Make a חַלּוֹן for daylight and a door
on the side to get in and out. This giant
תֵּבָה should be three floors high!"

נֹחַ worked on the תֵבָה for a long time. Part by part, stage after stage, נֹחַ carefully worked.

Will the lion have enough to eat?
Would the birds forget how to fly?
Would all the noise and all the joys
Fit in this תֵבָה three levels high?

When the giant תֵּבָה was ready G-d said to נֹחַ: "I saw that you are a צַדִּיק. Now you and your whole family need to go inside the תֵּבָה you built. Bring the animals in too!"

"Bring the Kosher animals in groups of seven. זָכָר and נְקֵבָה. Non-Kosher animals in pairs. One זָכָר and one נְקֵבָה. These are the only animals that will survive the great מַבּוּל and they will be the beginning of the future."

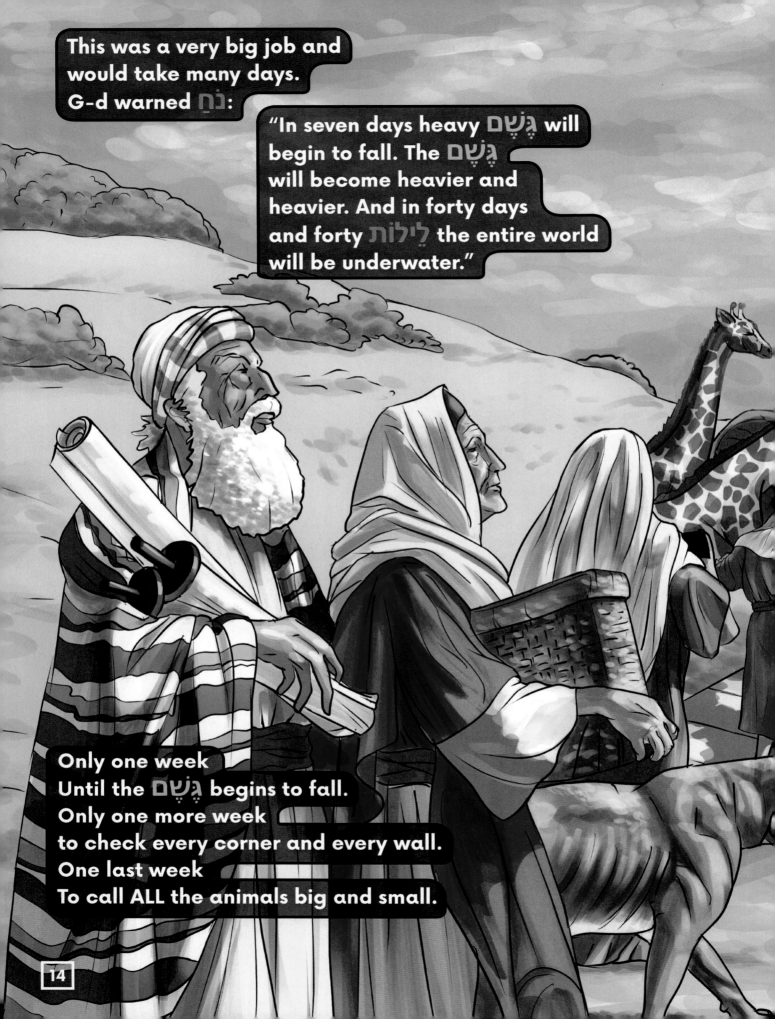

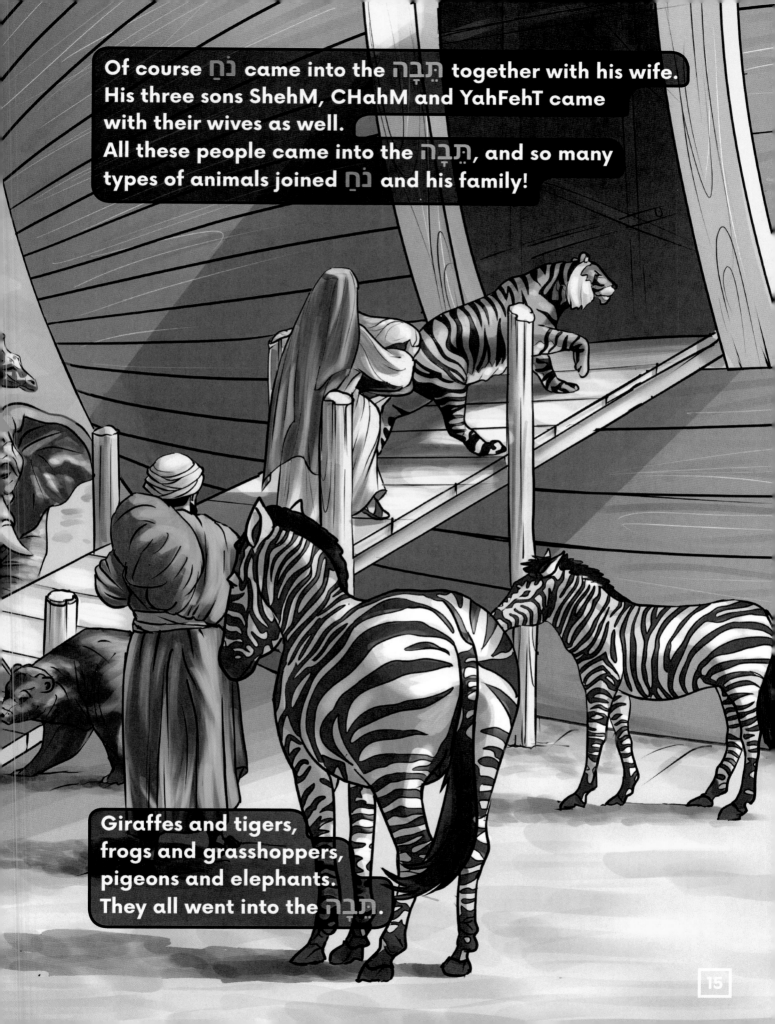

Of course נֹחַ came into the תֵבָה together with his wife. His three sons ShehM, CHahM and YahFehT came with their wives as well.
All these people came into the תֵבָה, and so many types of animals joined נֹחַ and his family!

Giraffes and tigers, frogs and grasshoppers, pigeons and elephants. They all went into the תֵבָה.

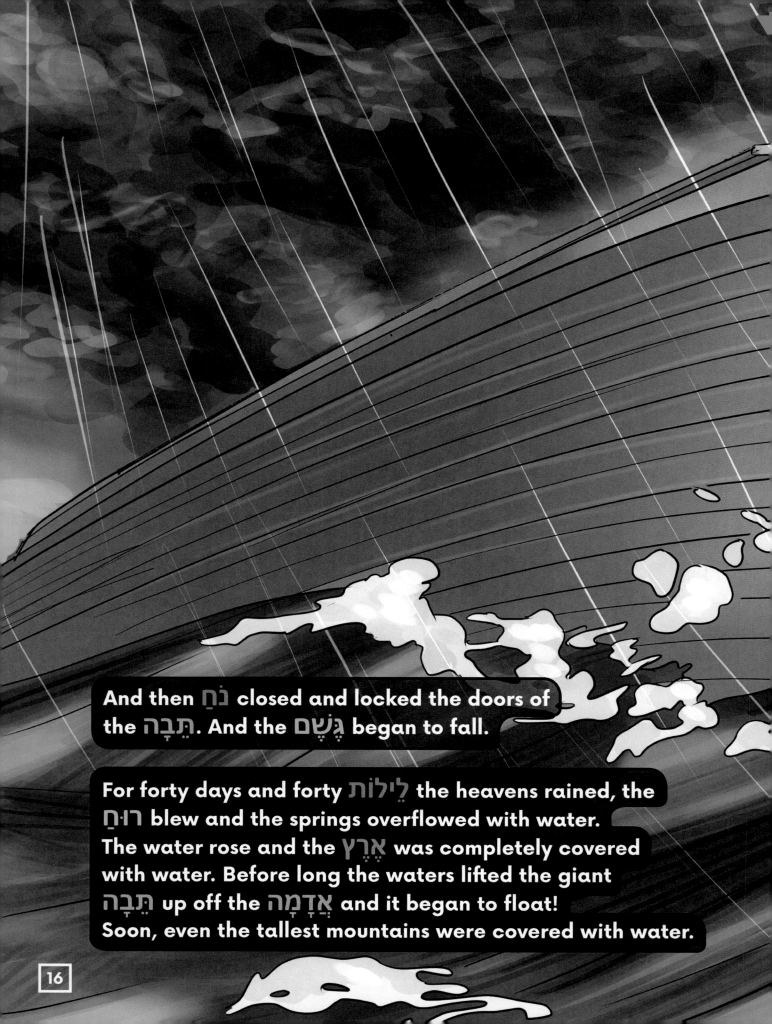

And then נֹחַ closed and locked the doors of the תֵּבָה. And the גֶּשֶׁם began to fall.

For forty days and forty לֵילוֹת the heavens rained, the רוּחַ blew and the springs overflowed with water. The water rose and the אֶרֶץ was completely covered with water. Before long the waters lifted the giant תֵּבָה up off the אֲדָמָה and it began to float! Soon, even the tallest mountains were covered with water.

Then for 150 days the water swelled and rose higher and higher and higher still. The only life in the whole world was afloat, in the great three story boat. נֹחַ and his family rushed around, taking care of all the animals who would have drowned.

And then something changed.

Five months after the מַבּוּל began, the water began to go away! It sank slowly into the אֶרֶץ and evaporated into the atmosphere.

Thump! The bottom of the תֵבָה skidded and rested on the tippiest top of the tall AhRahRahT Mountains!

After another three months, the tops of the shorter mountains were visible too.

נֹחַ threw open the חַלּוֹן to look outside at the new world.

Then נֹחַ gently brought the עוֹרֵב.
Little עוֹרֵב, little עוֹרֵב,
Tell us what you know
Fly out through the חַלוֹן
and see if something grows.
נֹחַ wanted the עוֹרֵב to check if the אֶרֶץ
had dried enough for them to leave the
תֵּבָה. The water had not yet dried and the
עוֹרֵב returned to rest his tired wings.

Some time later נֹחַ tried again.
Only this time he sent a יוֹנָה.
Little יוֹנָה, little יוֹנָה
tell us what you know
Fly out through this חַלּוֹן
Has anything started to grow?
But the יוֹנָה didn't even find a dry
place to rest, so she came back
to the תֵּבָה.

נֹחַ waited seven MORE days. He sent the יוֹנָה out again. Find a Home! Fly away little יוֹנָה! You will find shalom! This time the יוֹנָה flew out through the חַלוֹן and never returned. The water had dried!

One year and ten days after the great מַבּוּל began נֹחַ came out of the תֵּבָה. His whole family came out of the תֵּבָה. All the animals came out of the תֵּבָה.

A colorful קֶשֶׁת filled the שָׁמַיִם.
And so the world began anew.
G-d promised there would never again
be a great מַבּוּל in the entire world and
He created the beautiful קֶשֶׁת as a sign
of this promise.

Here are the Hebrew words from this *Easy Eevreet Story*:

נֹחַ   NohahCH - **NOAH**   p. 6,9,10,12,14,15, 16,18,22-27

צַדִּיק   TZahDeeYK - **RIGHTEOUS PERSON**   p. 6,12

אָדָם   'ahDahM - **MANKIND**   p. 6

'ahDahM is also the Hebrew version of
the name **ADAM**

רַע   Rah' - **EVIL**   p. 6

תֵּבָה   TehVahH - **ARK**   p. 9,10,11,12,15,16, 21,23,24,27

TehVahH can also mean a **BOX** or a **CHEST**.

חַלּוֹן   CHahLohN - **WINDOW**   p. 9,22,23,24,26

זָכָר   ZahCHahR - **MALE**   p. 13

נְקֵבָה   N-KehVahH - **FEMALE**   p. 13

KehSHehT can also mean an archer's bow or it can mean a hairband, depending on the context.

You did it! That was great reading. And you're all set with some rough weather vocabulary! Get ready to close the חַלוֹן before the רוּחַ does the job for you. After the גֶּשֶׁם you can look out for the קֶשֶׁת . What a treasure it is to see G-d's promise in the sky.

Hi!

My name is **Miiko.** I live in Be'er Sheva, Israel. My husband Aaron and I have nine kids: Menucha, Mendel, Dovi, Yisroel, Freida, Devora, Fitche, Geula, and Azaria.

I teach Hebrew reading with a fun little book called *Learn to Read Hebrew in 6 Weeks!*

My second book *The Hebrew Workbook* teaches readers to write in Hebrew.

The Promise of the Rainbow is part of a series of storybooks that teach Hebrew vocabulary to kids.

I'm so pleased to be a part of your Hebrew journey. If you have any questions or want to say hi please send me an email!
Miiko@LearnHebrew.tv

To the Parents

This book is designed to teach Hebrew vocabulary to people who already know how to read the Hebrew alphabet. While reading this Bible story in English you'll come across Hebrew words embedded in the text. Sound out the words and try to guess their meaning from the context. Check the key in the back of the book to see if you were right.

I've chosen to transliterate the names of the biblical characters mentioned in this story so that you'll learn the authentic Hebrew pronunciation of these biblical names.

Transliteration

The Promise of the Rainbow uses the same system of transliteration as my first book *Learn to Read Hebrew in 6 Weeks!*

I came up with a unique transliteration system. It's designed to have the reader pronouncing the Hebrew words accurately without ever having heard a Hebrew speaker pronounce those words.

Here's a breakdown of the system:

Each consonant is represented as a capital letter and each vowel by small letters.

The silent letters 'ahLehF (א) and 'ahYeeN (ע) are represented by an apostrophe (')

The silent vowel 'Sh-Vah' (:) is represented as a hyphen (-).

An important exception to make note of:
The CH does not represent the ch sound like in *chair* or *chest*. In fact, Hebrew doesn't have the ch sound like *chair* or *chest* at all.

The CH represents the letters CHehT(ח) and CHahF(כ) and Final ChahF(ך). These letters make a sound not found in the English language. It's a chokey sound that almost sounds like a kitten purring but much harsher. Think about the name of the composer Bach. From what my Spanish speaking students tell me, it's the same sound as the guttural J in Spanish.

Let's look at the first word in the Hebrew Scripture as an example of how my system works:

בְּרֵאשִׁית

I transliterate it:
B-Reh'SHeeYT

Others may transliterate Bereshit or Bresheet but then you wouldn't know if the vowels are long or short.

If you learned to read Hebrew using my other book, you are already well familiar with this system. But in case you learned to read Hebrew elsewhere, here's a key to make sure it's clear.

ו	ה	ד	ג	ב	בּ	א
V	H	D	G	V	B	'

ך	כ	כּ	י	ט	ח	ז
CH	CH	K	Y	T	CH	Z

ע	ס	ן	נ	ם	מ	ל
'	S	N	N	M	M	L

ר	ק	ץ	צ	ף	פ	פּ
R	K	TZ	TZ	F	F	P

ת	תּ	שׁ
T	T	SH

ִ	וֹ	וּ	ֶ	דָ
- ee	oh	oo	eh	ah

LEARN TO READ AND WRITE HEBREW WITH MY FUN AND EASY SYSTEM!

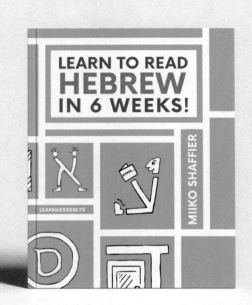

#1 BESTSELLERS
IN HEBREW LANGUAGE INSTRUCTION

- FUN MEMORY TRICKS
- 12 SIMPLE LESSONS
- PACED TO FINISH IN 6 WEEKS
- LEARN TO READ THE HEBREW BIBLE
- GREAT FOR ADULTS OR CHILDREN ALIKE
- CHARMING ILLUSTRATIONS TO MAKE LEARNING HEBREW A PLEASURE

MORE DETAILS AT LEARNHEBREW.TV

AVAILABLE AT AMAZON

Made in the USA
Middletown, DE
28 March 2023